Daphne Kitching writes and perform~
has been published in over for
(Macmillan), *Whizz Bang Ora*
I'm in a Mood Today (Oxford L
(Oxford University Press), *The*
Wishing Well, Weather (Schola
(Macmillan), *101 Favourite Poems*
(Collins), *I Love You Football* (Hc
Book of Christmas Poems (Oxford University Press), *I Remember, I*
Remember - A celebration of childhood in verse (Macmillan), and
Blood and Roses, British History in Poetry (Macmillan). Her
Christmas play, *Isn't he beautiful,* was published by Scripture Union
in the collection, *Maximus Mouse's Christmas Card and Other*
Christmas Plays. She has also written short stories to improve
auditory attention.

Daphne's first collection of poems, **As long as there are trees**
(ISBN 1 902039 10 6), was published in 2001 by Kingston Press.

Daphne now teaches pupils with Specific Learning Difficulties
(Dyslexia) after working for many years as a primary school teacher
in North Yorkshire. She is a member of the National Association of
Writers in Education.

Daphne was born in Scholes, Cleckheaton, West Yorkshire. She now
lives in East Yorkshire with her husband, David. They have three
children, James, John and Hannah.

Elaine Hill was born and brought up in Hull and was trained in fine
art at Hull and Maidstone art colleges, specialising in portraiture. She
has worked as a teacher and bookshop manager but currently works
from home on varied art commissions. Elaine is married to the vicar
of a busy parish in East Yorkshire!

While there are some good poems which are only for adults...there are no good poems which are only for children.

W. H. Auden

Spider-Flavoured Sausages

Family-flavoured poems by Daphne Kitching

ILLUSTRATIONS BY
Elaine Hill

With my best wishes,

Daphne Kitching

Published by Hands Up Books

British Library Cataloguing in Publication Data.
A catalogue record for this book is available from the British Library.

ISBN 095427104 - 1

This edition first published 2004
by
Hands Up Books
4, Sandringham Cottages,
Brantingham
HU15 1QH
East Riding of Yorkshire
Email: handsup@handsup.karoo.co.uk

Book design by Louise Morgan and Graham Denton

Printed in England by Central Print Services, Hull
Cover printed by Wyke Printers Ltd

Dedicated with love and thanks to my children,
James, John and Hannah
"The Thrilling Three"

For the Lord is good and his love endures for ever:
His faithfulness continues through all generations.
Psalm 100:5

CONTENTS

FUN - FLAVOURED

*Time is just waiting for you,
stretching out and waiting ...
deliciously.*

Come Camping

Come camping, come camping,
It's really great,
With spider-flavoured sausages
And slugs stuck to your plate.
There are earwigs in your Wellingtons
And ants sharing your bed,
The wasps you sprayed are fighting back
And targeting your head.
The hollow where you pitched your tent
Has turned into a bog,
And that dripping muddy monster
Is what used to be your dog.
Your clothes are cold and smelly,
Your sleeping bag feels damp,
It's a riot, it's sensational,
So come with us and camp!

Holiday Time

Holiday time is different
To any other time.
It's made up of hours and minutes
Like all time is,
But somehow they re-arrange themselves.
Holiday time is like elastic.
At the beginning of the holiday
The hours and minutes stretch out
So long that you think the days
Will go on forever.
So much time ahead of you,
So many things you can do,
And you don't need to rush because
Time is just waiting for you,
Stretching out and waiting...................
Deliciously,
At the beginning of the holiday.
But, then before you know it
It's Thursday afternoon
And you go home on Saturday.
And all Friday will be taken up
With packing and tidying and buying presents.
And you still haven't been on a boat,
Or made yourself sick on the Super Looper,
Or flown the Cockatoo kite you bought on Monday,
Or had a Knickerbocker Glory,
(You've never had a Knickerbocker Glory)
Time - the elastic version - has caught you by surprise
And snapped back to a very short length.
It's strange,
But holiday time is different.

3

Boat Dreams

Wobbly walking,
Thick warm coats,
Drips and splashes,
I love boats.

I dream of a boat to sail in,
I dream of a boat to row,
I dream of a boat with pedals
Or an engine to make it go.

All kinds of boats on rivers,
On ponds or out on the sea,
All kinds of fishing boats,
Leaky boats, wishing boats,
Dreams full of boats
And ME.

What next?

Read a story,
Watch TV,
Chase the cat
Or climb a tree?
It's quite good fun
To grow some cress,
But best of all
Let's make a MESS.

Splash the paint
And spill the glue,
Sprinkle glitter
All over YOU.
Wear your very oldest dress,
Then,
Make a marvellous,
Mixed up muddlesome,
Bound to get you
Into troublesome,
Splashing, splattering,
Rub-dub-dubblesome,
Spotted, stripy,
Rainbow coloursome,
Mega, multi,
Mountainous
MESS.

Recipe for Saturday Morning

Ingredients:
2 parents, sleeping in
1 brother, sprinkled with good mood powder
1 large dollop of children's programmes
1 tin, newly filled with Chocolate Fingers and Cookies
Cola or juice to mix
No homework
No clubs
No plans

What to do:

1. Leave the parents snoring softly - the longer the better.
2. Take the brother gently by the hand, making sure you do not disturb the good mood powder.
3. Creep carefully downstairs, do not roll or add noise.
4. Choose a programme and test for flavour.
5. Watch happily.
6. After a few minutes toss in one or two Chocolate Fingers and a Cookie.
7. Add Cola or juice a little at a time and mix in the mouth.
8. Enjoy for about two hours.

It is important not to stir the snoring parents as homework, clubs and plans would spoil this recipe.

Postcard

Wetnesday 14 Aufulgust

Dear Aunty Jane,
We're here again,
We're in our tent, we're in the rain.
It's such a lot of dripping fun,
and two weeks since we saw the sun.
How I wish that you were here
instead of me oh Aunty, dear.

Love from Holly Day.

Jane Goze
2A Sunny Place
E. Choliday
YDO NTWE

The Pancake Patternarius

The Pancake Patternarius,
Unique and therefore rarious,
He landed from thinairius
And ran.

All bubbleskin and various,
Sizzling, brown and scarious
Is the Pancake Patternarius
Of Pan.

He comes from Stir-and-pourius
To leave you wanting morius,
With lemon, syruporius
Or jam.

A monster maginarious
With swirls and dots delarious
Is the Pancake Patternarius
Of Pan.

FOOTBALL-FLAVOURED

I have football with my cornflakes,
I spread football on my toast...

Footballitis

I have football with my cornflakes,
I spread football on my toast,
I eat and breathe and sleep it,
It's the thing I dream of most.

Football posters in my bedroom,
Football stickers in my books
My hair is striped in red and white,
I love the way it looks.

I watch television football,
I play football in the park,
I imagine winning matches
In the sunshine, in the dark.

I write football poems and stories,
I count footballs in my maths,
I score goals into dustbins
I dribble Coke cans down the paths.

I have football with my cornflakes,
I spread football on my toast,
I eat and breathe and sleep it,
It's the thing I dream of most.

Not Everybody Likes Football

Not everybody likes football.
Even some boys don't.
And it doesn't mean you're soft,
Or that you should be left out of other things,
Or laughed at, or pointed at,
Or made to feel a fool.
It's just that not everybody likes football.

Not everybody likes football.
At least, not all the time.
And it doesn't mean you can't be friends,
Or share a joke,
Or come to play,
Or be one of the gang today.
It's just that not everybody likes football.

White Boots

If I had white boots
Like Beckham,
Maybe then I could play.
Maybe then I wouldn't trip up
Whenever the ball came my way.
Maybe the captain would pick me,
And I'd score with my very first kick.
The whole school would cheer
As goal number two
Found the net from my overhead flick.

Never again would I sit on the ball,
Or run the wrong way up the pitch,
Or pass to their striker, or let in six goals
Or have to lie down with a stitch,
If I had white boots
Like Beckham.

supporters log on

www. united plc
welcome to the website
our information's free
log on to discover
how successful clubs are run
shop on-line and meet the stars
see the cups they've won
browse through all the merchandise
our loyal fans requested
read the manager's account
of the night he was arrested
we encourage our great followers
to surf the net in red
buy our clothes and spread the word
support with heart and head
anything is possible
just grab your mouse and flick it
we offer you free access -
just don't request a ticket
for
a
match
as they are SOLD OUT
to business men and their wives
who don't know the captain's name

anyone want to log off?

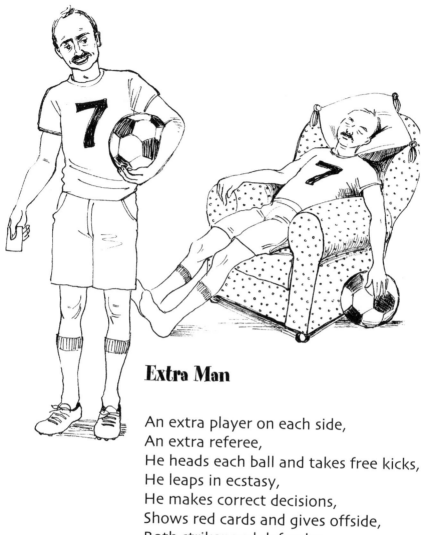

Extra Man

An extra player on each side,
An extra referee,
He heads each ball and takes free kicks,
He leaps in ecstasy,
He makes correct decisions,
Shows red cards and gives offside,
Both striker and defender
He is full of righteous pride.
He wears the shirt and looks the part,
(With very little hair)
He's every man for ninety minutes,
Then he collapses in his chair.

Dad's a star.

Captain to Captain

Winmoor School
Gamesborough
WE1 URo

Dear Mark and the boys of Matcham School team,

As Captain of Winmoor football team may I thank you
for the match. We all enjoyed the tussle and the goal
we managed to snatch! Sorry about all the bruises, and
your striker's broken left arm. Our defenders are
normally so careful that their tackles don't do any harm.

I expect you were all really upset that the goalie's nose
bled when it did, and that the full back, when making
his challenge, scored a stunning home goal from his
skid.

Although it was quite hard to beat you, we feel that our
victory was fair. We hope that your boys are good
losers ----- as for us, we'll just let down our hair!

Looking forward to the return match next season,

Best wishes,

Hannah,

on behalf of the team,:- Julie, Suzanne, Lucy, Emma,
Molly, Sarah, Liz, Isabel, Katie and Becky.

16

PEOPLE-FLAVOURED

To trick with and trust with...

Look at ME

Mum's feeding the baby,
Dad's asleep in bed,
There's no one here to play so
I'll amuse myself instead.

A work of art is called for,
Something big and bright,
In purple paint and sparkles
To liven up the night.

They're bound to be more cheerful
When I call them in to see
A walking, talking masterpiece,
A purple-painted ME.

William

William is a little boy
Who's very hard to find,
He rushes here and over,
Out and under and behind.

And as he rushes onwards
He's quite possible to miss,
Then, when you least expect it,
He'll rush to meet you with a kiss.

Just like

Just like Jane,
Just like Jack,
Drives me up a tree,
Just because I'm youngest
Means I'm never
Just like me.

Rosie Ronaldo

Rosie Ronaldo
With corkscrew curls,
Jokes with the boys,
Giggles with the girls.
Melon-slice grin,
Chocolate eyes,
Mountains of fun
In miniature size.

Rosie Ronaldo,
Star of the show,
Her *Yes* means *Yes*
And her *No* means *No*.
The same at the start,
As she is at the end,
Rosie Ronaldo,
My best friend.

With

To shop with
And share with
And show off your hair with

To chat with
And cheer with
And chase away fear with

To plan with
And play with
Be pleased you can stay with

To trick with
And trust with
Completely and just with

Your friend.

Saying Goodnight

Sharing a room with a sister,
Who's older and thinks she has rights,
Isn't easy when rights are unequal,
And she has control of the lights.

Because she was born first she chooses
If we should talk, read or fight,
But I won't go to sleep till I know that I've been
The last one to whisper, *Goodnight.*

No I won't go to sleep till I know that I've been
The last one to whisper, *Goodnight.*

It starts when she switches the light off,
And calls out *Goodnight.* I reply.
Each of us knows that we must say it last,
Though neither really knows why.

The *Goodnights* fly to the ceiling,
They bounce quickly down to the floor
For at least half an hour the *Goodnights* come and go,
Passing bookcase and wardrobe and door.

I wait till she thinks that I'm sleeping,
Till she thinks that her victory's complete,
Then I whisper *Goodnight,* and the real truth is known
By the darkness and me and the sheet.

Yes I whisper *Goodnight,* and the real truth is known
By the darkness and me and the sheet.

Aunties' Kisses

Why do aunties want to kiss you
When they come and when they go?
Why do they always want to kiss you,
Slip-slap quick or slimy slow?

I love my auntie, she's the one who
Buys toy mice, tin drums and tricks,
But how I hate those last embraces,
Garlic, mints and pink lipsticks.

Why do they want to squeeze and hold
And make a fuss before they leave?
Don't they know that sloppy kisses
Just get wiped off on my sleeve?

Grandad's Flowers

Those flowers
Pink, with daisy faces
Came from Grandad's.
He grew them from seeds
In his greenhouse,
Looked after them like babies,
Loved them,
Loved flowers and football and special toffee.

The toffee's gone,
The team's been relegated,
But in the garden
Grandad's flowers grow.

A Place Without Footprints

I'm searching for a place
Without footprints,
But I'm the youngest child.

Whatever I try,
Wherever I go,
Whatever I choose,
One of them has already
Succeeded,
Been there,
Chosen first.
I'm just a comparison,
Usually unfavourable.
Born to follow,
To repeat the pattern,
The footprints are never mine.

But I'll keep moving,
Hoping the direction is new,
Hoping that one day
A space will appear
Like a fresh snowfall,
Untouched,
Un-noticed by the others,
As I'm searching for a place
Without footprints,
As I'm searching for a place
To plant mine.

CREATURE - FLAVOURED

Shake in your own imagination,
Season well with fantasy and fun...

Silent Witness

Swimming round the goldfish bowl O,
Fairground prize, a golden solo,
Ready, steady, quick, quick, slow O,
Watching all who come and go O.

Humans think that I'm on show O,
That's a joke, ho, ho, ho, ho, O,
I see things they'd love to know O,
Shall I tell them? Oh, no, no, O.

We're very much alike

We're very much alike,
My owner and me.
He wakes up in the evening
After dozing through the day at his desk,
And he comes upstairs
Into the converted loft where I live.
He spends hours cycling aimlessly
On a bike that doesn't move,
Or rowing on a boat
Which has never seen water.
Then he takes out his secret store of food,
In his case, Mars Bars which he keeps
Hidden in the filing cabinet.
He nibbles away at them,
Twitching and glancing around anxiously
As he nibbles, before shredding the wrapper
So that no-one will ever know.
Then he tries to escape,
But instead of gnawing and rattling
The bars of his cage,
He switches on his computer
And escapes from the real world
Onto the Internet.
Exercising, chewing, shredding, escaping,
Oh yes, we're very much alike,
My owner and me.

Spider

There's a spider near the toilet,
Under a plastic pot.
I hope he doesn't suffocate,
I hope he's not too hot.
Scared to try to catch him,
Scared to set him free,
Which of us has problems,
The captured one or me?

Wasp (Kenning)

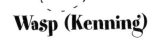

Classroom scarer
Panic bearer
Buzzing rhymer
Window climber
Picnic spoiler
Temper boiler
Summer winger
Stripy stinger
Ouch!

Dinosaur Dream Recipe

Ingredients:

A handful of prehistoric fossil dust
A sprinkling of teeth (all sharp and thin)
A scattering of scales and just the same amount of spikes
A roll of best quality dried skin
1 landscape of swamps and caves and forests
1 climate, warm and misty, baked with sun
Shake in your own imagination
Season well with fantasy and fun

How to make your dinosaurs:-

Stir the fossil dust
And add the teeth and scales and spikes
Wrap loosely in the skin
And brush with sun
Turn them in the heat
And then dip them in the swamp
Dream them into life
Then turn and RUN!

SCHOOL-FLAVOURED

They want to drive their teachers
Gently, daily up the walls...

School Visit

Like a visitor from another world
Came the cuckoo to our assembly.
He should never have been there at all
But we were glad he was.

A voice without a body
Had been the cuckoo to us, till then.
That day they came to school together,
And we met mystery.

Stunned by our window
His faulty radar delivered him to us,
And for a moment, between maths and
playtime,
We shared our lives.

He was large and grey and wonderful,
We were stilled and awed and mesmerised,
Gazing at the invisible,
Aware of the privilege.

Until, regaining strength,
He left us,
And re-entered his own kingdom,
And everything and all of us were different.

The year is like ice-cream

The year is like ice-cream, or jelly or juice,
It comes in four flavours.
While you're tasting one
You can't help remembering the one you had before,
Or looking forward to the next one.
Thinking about the best bits,
Remembering the flavours.

The flavour of Spring is
A new present still to unpack,
Muddy brown turning to
Growing green,
Lambs and catkins and frogspawn
Leaping from winter wrappings
With a spring to start off the year.

The flavour of summer is
Shorts and summer dresses,
Sports Day, SATs and end of term fun,
Holidays and wasps,
The sticky stillness of days without darkness,
Sand in your food and on your feet.
Summer, the smile of the year.

The flavour of Autumn is
Polished shoes and conkers,
New term, new class, new teacher,
New books without blotches or botches,
New start.
Paint-box world in falling swirls,
Put on more clothes as autumn takes hers off.

The flavour of Winter is
Soup and chestnuts, curry and stew,
A white world splashed with Christmas red,
Wet shoes, wet hair, wet clothes and coughs,
Indoor playtimes, television home-times,
Slippers on, sweaters on, fire on full,
Winter, closing the door of the year.

Do Elephants Have Spelling Tests?

Elephants never forget, they say,
But what do elephants have to remember?

Do they have
Spelling tests,
Tables,
And piano scales?

Do they have
Games kit
Indoor shoes
And books?

Do they have
A lunch box
Word cards
And signed notes?

Do they have
Ingredients
For lessons
When they cook?

Do they have to
Wash hands
Tidy desks
And work trays?

Do they have to
Listen and then
Do the things
They heard?

Do they have to
Concentrate
Working hard
At school all day

And then at home
Remember and
Repeat every word?

If elephants had to do all this
Surely even they would sometimes forget.

Testing

They test us
They say, to find out what we're learning,
They test us
We know, to find out who's the best.

They test us
On Mondays and Wednesdays and Fridays,
On Tuesdays and Thursdays we train
For the test.

They test us
On spelling and reading and writing,
They test us on how to subtract and to add.

They test us
On attitude, style and behaviour
They label us
Good, satisfactory or bad.

They tell us
That testing is not so important,
They say we're all equal whatever we do.

They tell us that test scores and labels don't matter,
Then test us again
So we know that they do.

Grand, it was

Last term we went to Narnia
At three o'clock each day.
Through the wardrobe door, one by one,
To sit on cotton wool snow
Beneath cardboard trees,
Watched by a tissue paper Aslan and fake-fur fauns,
As we discovered how Christmas came back.

Before that we had the Secret Garden
Its door hidden under Ellie's ivy,
Which we had to unlock with the rusty key
Sam found by the cloakroom door
The day we started the book.
Half an hour, every day, living in Yorkshire
With Mary and Diccon and Colin.
Aye that we did. Grand, it was.

This term we've shared Stig's Dump,
The entrance covered by bark-rubbed branches
We had to push aside to crawl through after science.
Junk, old tyres strewn with dark netting,
Dried up leaves we'd collected and scattered welcomed us.
Bindweed and crepe paper creepers tickled
While we lived the adventures
And hid from the Snargets till home time.

Now there's just the empty corner of the room.
The old 3-section, folding play-house
Leans against the wall, scrubbed bare.
No Dump, no Narnia, no Secret Garden.
The last day of the summer term,
And we're moving up to Year 5
Where the classroom's just a classroom.

Discussion

Teacher:

"I'm disturbed and dismayed and disgusted,
I'm distressed and disgruntled as well,
Your writing is so disappointing
And you seem quite unable to spell.
You disobey lists of instructions,
You disregard "b"s, "d"s and "p"s,
Your bag is disguised as a war-zone
Its contents in the grip of disease.
Your reading books keep disappearing
In the most disagreeable way,
I dislike your dismal excuses,
But which one's on offer today?"

Pupil:

"I'm dyslexic."

Asking Annie

There are thirty-one children in our class.
Some don't want to be noticed or asked questions,
Some like to be noticed and try to answer questions,
Some don't mind.
And then there's Annie,
Hand piercing the ceiling,
Annie always has the answer,
Annie always knows.

Miss Fairhead understands our differences.
Miss Fairhead's all for equal rights and inclusiveness.
She always says "human" instead of "man" kind
And makes sure girls have equal time on the football
pitch.
In lessons you can see her looking round
Trying to encourage the quiet ones,
Trying not always to ask Annie.

But whenever the Head comes in,
Or Inspectors inspect,
Or Governors get involved,
You can sense the battle begin,
The battle for the behaviour of Miss Fairhead.
In the end, there's no way she'll be let down by Lottie,
Or embarrassed by Sam Spratt.
No, when the chalk-talk is tested
She won't risk it,
She'll ask Annie,

Annie always has the answer,
Hands-up Annie always knows.

Dear Mrs Murgatroyd

The Boyes-Wilby Boys School
Weel Sorthamout Road
Orgetriddofham.

Dear Mrs Murgatroyd,

Your Barry had a pain, and as I watched he shrivelled up and vanished down the drain. I know this will distress you, and you 'll really miss your son, but please, may I implore you not to have another one.

The teachers all agree that Barry's problems were severe, and when they heard he'd shrivelled, simply couldn't help but cheer. For Barry troubled teachers, gave them breakdowns, stress and spots. His hyperactive antics led to scientific plots.

Shrinking powder recipes were found, I must explain, on a table near the spot where Baz slipped down the dirty drain.

Barry's inability to keep his fingers still, brought trouble when his messing made the shrinking powder spill. He shrivelled and he went bright green when sliding down the drain. Though sad for you, the staff all hope he won't expand again.

Now I'm sending home his gym kit, and I hope you will be strong, but even if he re-appears, the sizes will be wrong. And as you wash and scrub the kit, removing all the stains, just smile and think of Barry causing havoc down the drains.

Yours sincerely,

(Head of Boys)   SH Rinker.

Mrs Brady or What?

There is something very dreadful,
Very dreadful in our school,
So dreadful that it makes you want to shrink,
It appears, to terrorise us,
At 12 o'clock each day,
A monster in a startling shade of pink.

It shrieks and screams and wobbles,
Flaps its arms and wags its head,
It forces us to swallow Brussels sprouts,
It chases us outside
To torment us as we play,
And never speaks a single word,
But SHOUTS.

This descendent of a dragon
From a prehistoric age,
Outside school is simply known
As Mrs Brady,
And the nostril-flaring horror,
That Very Dreadful Something,
Pretends that it is just a dinner lady.

Not another school trip

When it rained on the way to the famous fossil beach
And Cressida Critchlow was sick on the coach,
And Mr Jones realised we had left the packed lunches at school,
It seemed that this would be just like any other school trip,
Forgettable.
Until we found the fossil.

We had combed the beach,
Found bits of belemnites, mostly without their points,
Found devil's toe-nails, dull and common,
And a few ordinary shells.
Nothing exciting enough to make us forget
The damp patches spreading across our shoulders
Inside our 100% waterproof jackets.

Then someone gave Mr Jones this piece of Jurassic rock -
Light grey, the suggestion of a fossil on its edge -
Just like we'd been told to look for,
About the size of a hand.

Mr Prehistoric-Safety-Goggles-Jones
Split it with one blow of his fossil hammer,
And there it was,
A perfect ammonite,
Come into the light
For the first time for millions of years.
Sprinkled with Fool's Gold glitter,
Our eyes the first to see it.
Shining spiral sunshower,
Released from its pressed-earth prison
Like a Jurassic genie,
Ancient yet instantly new.

Time held its breath, as if we were in a photograph,
We looked and looked
At beauty on the beach,
In the rain,
And we knew we would remember.

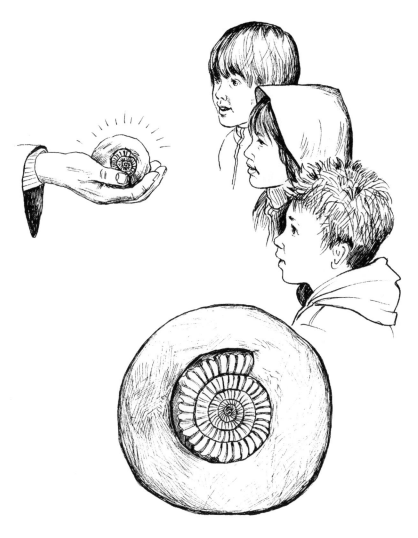

Sharing

A generous girl from Year Two
Mixed up measles with mumps and the 'flu,
I'll share my diseases,
She said between sneezes,
With you, and with you, and with you.

Thursday Terror Day

It's Thursday, worst Day,
It's Thursday, no!
It's Thursday, terror day,
Don't want to go.
It's Thursday, dinner day,
It's Thursday, noon,
It's Thursday, poison day,
Torture by prune.

Let them

They want to play, well let them,
They want to talk, that's fine,
They want to shred their school
reports,
Let them do it - I'll do mine.
They want to ban school uniform,
PE and mental sums,
They want to do away with tests,
To flick school dinner crumbs.

They want to drop their pencils,
Lose their rubbers, burst new balls,
They want to drive their teachers
Gently, daily up the walls.
They want to fall off chairs for fun
And paint the floor bright red,
And save their worst performance
For the visit of The Head.

Well, let them, let them, let them,
Let them do just as they please,
It's all so entertaining,
And they *only* mean to tease.
After many years of teaching
This new thinking is inspired,
But I'll let the others do it
This September.

I've retired!

HORRID-FLAVOURED

Spaghetti worms, maggot rice,
Slimy mushroom slugs...

Recipe for Mini-Beast Burgers

Ingredients:-

Spaghetti worms
Maggot rice
Slimy mushroom slugs
Pasta snails
Tomato blood
Prune and raisin bugs

Mix and mash,
Then liquidise with grub-infested gin,
Blend and beat and boil the beasts
To stir the flavours in.
Garnish them with spider's legs,
Toast a mouldy roll,
Enjoy with Alkaseltzers
Near a bucket or a bowl.

Picking

Spots
Toes
Scabs
Nose
Picking's all the rage.
Just when no-one's looking
Is a skill that comes with age.

Wonder Wax

Ear-wax is so wonderful,
Smooth and toffee gold,
Roll it in your fingers
Then leave it to grow cold
Collect it from your neighbours,
Press it into tins,
Label it organic
Then feed it to the twins.
Use it on the furniture,
Polish your new sandals,
Start a new designer craze,
Give ear-wax Christmas candles.

Pot Luck

Ingredients:-

7 money spiders
1 old rabbit's foot
3 black cats
4 horseshoes
1 sweep (complete with soot)

What to do:-

Toss them all together,
Add ancient charms,
Stir well.
Liquidise (including eyes),
Ignore the nasty smell.
Shred some four-leaved clovers,
Sprinkle in the pan.

Invite some friends to eat with you -
Good luck to those who can.

RIDDLE AND RHYME -FLAVOURED

*I start and I finish,
Time is in my hands...*

Riddleferee

I whistle while I work,
While I work I play cards,
My red means go not stop,
I receive no payment for the kicks I give,
People like them and want more,
My helpers run on lines and are trained,
I take part in games
But never win, never lose,
I start and finish,
Time is in my hands.

IT ('s) a Riddle

Log on with no danger of burning,
My mouse eats no cheese,
My web has no spiders
My net catches no fish,
Surf without sea
If you recognise me.

Humpty Together Again

Humpty Dumpty
After his fall
Built himself up
By eating the wall,
Brick after brick
After brick after brick,
Plus thirty King's Men,
Before he was sick.

Mary Meals

Mary had a little lamb
Who ate her up for lunch,
Mary Mince and Mary Chops
And Minty Mary Munch.

Baa, Baa, Black Deeds

Baa, baa, black sheep
You're looking rather fat,
You've casseroled the Master,
The Dame and Fluff the cat,
The little boy turned awkward
And swore to tell the police,
So you stuffed him in the third bag
And smothered him with fleece.

Colour Clue Haiku

(5-7-5 syllables)

Anger! Danger! Stop!
Colour of warnings and blood,
Cheerful, glowing blaze.

Prize fish from fairgrounds,
Shiny precious wedding rings,
Kings, crowns and treasure.

Outdoor number one,
Envy and sickness cause this,
Yellow and blue mixed.

Royal, sky, navy,
Feeling sad or unhappy,
Police car's flashing light.

Tongues, toes, pigs (or ham)
Girls are often dressed in this,
Boys can wear it too.

Roads, mist, November,
Image of fading dullness,
Lifting black with white.

Cheerfulness and fruit,
Bills of ducks and male blackbirds,
Our favourite juice.

Fluffy hen babies,
Shining gift of the bright sun,
Dusters and grapefruit.

Acrostics

Antagonizes
Niggles
Grows
Explodes
Ruins

Crumbs
All over
Keep
Eating

Someone
Tells
Or
Reads to
You

Kenning

Carpet brusher
Grime crusher
Noisy worker
Cupboard lurker
Crumb gobbler
Floor wobbler
Greedy sucker
Treasure plucker
Switch on

Vacuum cleaner

FLAVOURS OF THE PAST

*Sometimes, it seems in the still of the night
that time stops in the heart of my being...*

Blacksmith's Luck

Horseshoes may be lucky,
But for me the luck was bad,
I made them by the hundred,
That was the job I had.
As tractors replace horses,
The shire is disappearing,
Flesh and blood evolves
To metal skin and power steering.

Vikings (Kenning)

Northern raiders
Old invaders
Seafarers
People scarers
Saga tellers
Red-haired yellers
Place namers
War gamers
Fierce fighters
Kenning writers
Vikings

Night Thoughts of Oliver Cromwell

I signed the death warrant that finished the King,
My name was third on the list.

He ruled without parliament, for power and gain,
He taxed and demanded and never explained,
He schemed with the Catholics in Ireland and Spain
And stirred up unrest in the country.
We Parliamentarians had to take charge,
Under God, our duty was clear,
To bring in a new constitution by law,
That would stand through the tests of the years,
And guarantee peace for the country.

We were right, I am sure, and I have no regrets,
The future is now with the people,

But sometimes, it seems in the still of the night
That time stops in the heart of my being,
And all that exists is this sentence of mine,
That I signed for the death of the King.

Carisbrooke

Now flowers grow wild at Carisbrooke
Where once the King was kept,
And children wander freely,
With blue sky as the ceiling,
In the room that was his prison.

The stones soak today's sun
Into secrets they will never share,
The plans of his people to free him,
Which he couldn't, wouldn't pursue,
The germination of the unthinkable seed of doubt,
Suppose he were not untouchable?

Winter days and nights within the castle walls,
Waiting for the warrant of change.
Death to give birth to the democracy
That brings these children to wander and wonder
And look up at his window,
And see the flowers that grow wild now,
At Carisbrooke.

*King Charles 1 was held prisoner at Carisbrooke Castle on The Isle of
Wight, before his execution on 30 January 1648. Today a plaque marks
a window through which he unsuccessfully attempted to escape.*

Homecoming, 1946

That's my Dad, and he's smiling,
In his uniform, smiling and smart.

Part of all my remembering life
Like waking and falling asleep.
I talk to him and I talk him back.
He listens and smiles on,
Dusty in the sunshine,
Invisible in the blackout,
But always there, always the same.

He's patient and loving
And brave, people say.
So I know what he's like.
And he doesn't swear and shout,
He doesn't fill the air with smoke and anger,
Or disturb our days and nights,
Or change the way our world works.
He doesn't fill our quiet space
With questions we cannot answer,
Questions no one can answer.

My Dad has nothing to do with
The man downstairs who came last week,
Wearing a suit and hot eyes
That travel without us.

No, *that's* my Dad, and he's smiling,
In his uniform, smiling and smart.

D-Day 2004

Sixty years since D-Day
And the veterans went back,
With their straight backs
And bent backs,
With their medals
And memories.

The sun shone,
The flags flew
With sadness and pride
In old hearts still beating
To the tune composed
On the beaches of Normandy,
On the beaches of hearts broken.

They stood in the sunshine,
And the world acknowledged its liberators
In a pause of perception
Of history passing from people to pages.

And the world watched
And wondered at such men.

MIXED FLAVOURS

*New days to colour
and the crayons are mine...*

NOISE

CDs, radios, televisions, videos,
Phone bells, door bells, school bells
Ring.

Computers, keyboards, fruit machines and game boys,
Electronic everythings zing, zing,
Zing.

Fridges, freezers, dishwashers and toasters,
Hair dryers, hand dryers, tumble dryers
Buzz.

Karaoke, wind-chimes, cousin Danny's nursery rhymes,
Everywhere and everyday shouting life at
Us.

Football crowds, extra loud, supermarket canned songs,
Motor bikes, tractors, supersonic
Jets.

Cockerels in the country, heavy rock at traffic lights,
House and fire and car alarms, attention-seeking
Pets.

Gadgets, machinery, animals, music,
Grown ups, aliens, girls and
Boys

Joining in, making more, adding to it every day,
The whizzing, whirring, wonderful world of
NOISE.

Days

Thrilling days
Boring days
Longed-for days
Dreaded days
In days
Out days
Stormy days and fine,

New days to colour
And the crayons are mine.

Birthdays
School days
Holidays
Growing days
Learning days
Remembered days
Days to rush about,

I wonder what will happen
When all the days run out?

When?

In a minute,
Later,
One day,
Maybe,
Soon,
I haven't time this morning,
Perhaps this afternoon.

We'll really do it sometime,
Next week,
Next month,
Next year,
Now I'd like to be with you,

That's strange,
There's no one here.

Out for a meal

Don't like salad,
Don't like fish,
Don't like mushrooms
Or pasta in a dish,
Don't like pizza
Not even in my dreams,
The only things I like
Are chips and ice-cream.

Chips and ice-cream,
Chips and ice-cream,
Please can I have
Chips and ice-cream.

Smile Invader Rap

I am eating my packed lunch,
I am biting a pear,
When I feel the strangest feeling
Ever felt anywhere,
There is movement in my mouth
And it doesn't feel right,
There's a wibbling and a wobbling
When I'm wanting to bite.
There's a dripping
          and a
               dropping,
Dripping
        drops
             that are red,
There is something sort of scary
Going on in my head.
As I look in Sammy's mirror
Something lands in my lap,
And my smile has been invaded
By a gummy great gap,

A gummy great gap,

Yes my smile has been invaded
By a gummy great gap.

Supermarket Song

In the supermarket, I always try
To think of a word for everything that we buy.

Cornflakes crackle,
Crisps crunch,
Mars bars melt,
Mint sweets munch.
Sausages sizzle,
Satsumas spray,
Baked bread breathes
As we're waiting to pay.

When shopping's boring, why not try
To think of a word for everything that you buy?

FESTIVAL FLAVOURED

...Showing us life in your beautiful face

Countdown

Five months,
Four months,
Three months,
Two months,
One more month to wait,
I'm counting down from being seven
And up to being eight.

Three weeks,
Two weeks,
One week,
One day,
It's here, it's here at last,
My day of days,
My birthday,
And it's whizzing by so fast.

Birthday cards,
Birthday presents,
Birthday candles,
Birthday cake,
Birthday party,
Birthday bingeing,
Birthday bedtime tummy ache.

And though it's perfect being eight,
A new thought's crossed my mind....
In eleven months and thirty days
Exactly, I'll be nine.

74

Under the table, after the Christening

There are Godfathers, great-aunts and uncles,
Grandparents doting and kind,
For whom tables are tables are tables
Though they open and broad be of mind.

Tables, to them, have a function,
To eat from, behave at and set,
To pull up a chair and sit down at,
Using manners they *never* forget.

They know nothing of sub-table magic,
Of the rivers that flow past their feet,
Of battles with dragons whose breath cooked their
lunch,
And who might melt them all with their heat.

They might miss their Godsons and daughters,
They might feel things crawl over their toes,
They might hear sub-clothian giggling sounds,
Catch a glimpse of a well-picked young nose.

Oh, Godfathers, great-aunts and uncles,
Grandparents doting and kind,
Resist the temptation to lift up the cloth
On a world you are too old to find.

Rock-a-bye

Rock-a-bye baby
The world is your cradle,
The wind only blows
If you speak the word,
Angels will rock you
And sing to God's glory,
The message of peace
And goodwill shall be heard.

Rock a bye baby
The stars are your baubles,
Crafted by you
Then set into space,
Born into weakness
You travel beside us,
Showing us life
In your beautiful face.

A Shepherd in need of an Angel

He didn't want to be there,
He was cold and lonely and sad,
He hadn't chosen shepherding,
It was just the job he had.
He was a shepherd in need of an angel.

But because he was there, he saw them,
In a sky full of songs and of light,
Angels, who needed a listener
To share the good news of the night.
They were angels in need of a shepherd.

And after he'd been to the stable,
The reflection of love in his face,
There was peace and contentment in being
A shepherd and in the right place.
A shepherd so glad of the angels.

A Shining Time

The moon, the starlit sparkles of frost,
Dressed-up trees with lights,
City streets and superstores
On December, shop-late nights,
Schools and homes, trimmed and bright,
Windows of tinsel and lace,
The birth of wonder, joy and hope
Shining from the face of a child,
Shining from his face,

Christmas is a shining time.

Wise Men

Once there were some wise men.
They didn't know the way,
But they were looking for it.
They followed the star.

They were scholars, they were searchers,
Who they didn't know the truth,
But they were looking for it.
They followed the star.

Although they were wise, they were puzzled,
They didn't know the meaning of life,
But they were looking for it.
They followed the star.

The star stopped over Jesus.

They were wise men,
They were wise men looking for
The way, the truth and the meaning of life.
They found Jesus.

Acknowledgements

Kersplosh, Kersplash, Kersplat!, Ron Heapy, OUP, 2001, (Captain to Captain)

Are we nearly there yet?, Brian Moses, Macmillan, 2002, (Come Camping and Holiday Time). Also published as a Macmillan audio-book, with poems read by Stephen Tompkinson and Emma Chambers (2003)

My Mum's Put Me On The Transfer List, Football Poems, chosen by John Foster, OUP, 2002, (Footballitis and White Boots)

Taking My Human For a Walk, Roger Stevens, Macmillan, 2003, (Silent Witness and We're Very Much Alike)

I Love You Football, Poems about the beautiful game, Tony Bradman, Hodder Wayland Children's Books, 2003, (supporters log on)

I Remember, I Remember, A celebration of childhood in verse, Brian Moses, Macmillan, 2003, (A Place Without Footprints)

My First Oxford Christmas Book of Christmas Poems, John Foster, OUP, 2003, (Rockabye)

Dinos, Dodos and Other Dead Things, Brian Moses, Macmillan, 2003, (Blacksmith's Luck)

Blood and Roses, British History In Poetry, Brian Moses, Macmillan, 2004, (Night Thoughts of Oliver Cromwell)

The Trying Flapeze, John Foster, OUP, 2004, (Colour Clue Haiku)

Dinosaur Dream, Oxford Routes to Writing, OUP, 2004, (Dinosaur Dream Recipe, Riddle (vacuum cleaner), Supermarket song)

Chips and Ice Cream, Oxford Routes to Writing, OUP, 2004, (an edited version of Recipe for Saturday Morning, CAKE Acrostic, Out for a Meal.)

Poems for My Best Friend, Susie Gibbs, OUP, 2004, (With)

Disgusting Poems, Paul Cookson, MacMillan, 2004, (WonderWax)